WHEAL JANE

The Final Mining Years

JOHN PECK

HALSGROVE

First published in Great Britain in 2012

British Library Cataloguing-in-Publication Data
A CIP record for this title is available from the British Library

ISBN 978 0 85704 095 4

HALSGROVE
Halsgrove House,
Ryelands Business Park,
Bagley Road, Wellington, Somerset TA21 9PZ
Tel: 01823 653777   Fax: 01823 216796
email: sales@halsgrove.com

Part of the Halsgrove group of companies
Information on all Halsgrove titles is available at: www.halsgrove.com

Printed and bound in China by Everbest Printing Co Ltd

Contents

Foreword

One other interesting aspect that emerges from a detailed consideration of Cornish mining history is the great and abiding tenacity of the men engaged in it. There was – and, to a lesser degree, there still remains today – an inborn love of mining...'

D.B. Barton. *A History of Tin Mining and Smelting in Cornwall*

THE WHEEL OF FORTUNE that has by turns over the centuries dictated the rise and fall of Cornwall's mining industry slowly ground to a final halt towards the end of the twentieth century. While today rising world prices provide glimmers of a resurgence, the decaying remains of the industry largely survive in the form of heritage sites and in folk memories.

In this book the photographer John Peck records the final years of work at Wheal Jane, sited in the heart of Cornwall at Baldhu near Chacewater, a mine that had been worked for tin and other minerals since the mid eighteenth century. What began as a invitation to take photographs of the mine for an exhibition turned into a prime means of employment, and more than that, John became someone whom the miners themselves trusted to make an honest record of their working lives and, when it came to it, to document their protests running up to the mine's eventual closure.

Photography underground, often in poor and potentially dangerous conditions, takes a special skill. Having such a photographic record at all is of great historic value; that many of the pictures included here transcend mere reportage and become images of artistic excellence is a major achievement.

Simon Butler FRSA

Introduction

FROM AN EARLY AGE I had a keen interest in photography and rock climbing. My first trip underground was in the Mendip Hills with some climbing friends. We got lost but after eight hours finally found the exit. I remember stating that I was never going underground again. However, being only 18 years old I soon recovered from the experience and managed a few more trips.

In the late 1960s I moved to Cornwall with my young family and set up a business as a wedding and family photographer in Chacewater, near Truro. I began to take an interest in mining and I explored a few disused mines and enjoyed the adventure. I then met an assistant surveyor from Wheal Jane, a mine only two miles from where I lived, who told me they were advertising for a photographer to take photographs for an exhibition I was very interested. This seemed to be my dream job.

Apparently at the interview all the other photographers had stated they would use 35mm cameras to take the pictures. However, I thought that if these photographs were for an exhibition they would need to be taken on a medium format camera which would give a much larger negative. Luckily the mine manager agreed with me and I got the job.

I was employed for one job for which I would be paid £25.00 to produce six underground pictures and six pictures taken on the surface. I knew nothing about mining but hoped that the sense of adventure I felt when underground would get me through. Luckily when I went underground I always had a minder, without this I would have spent a lot of time wandering about the many seemingly endless mine passages.

Whilst I was completing this job there was an accident in the mine and I was asked to photograph the site. Prior to this the mine had relied on drawings and diagrams from the surveying department. Both the union and the management were pleased with the resulting photographs and from this date I was then on standby to be called if a serious accident occurred. This incident showed that good photographs could be taken despite the conditions that existed underground. The exhibition photographs also proved to be successful.

In 1978 the Canadian company who ran nearby Mount Wellington Mine pulled out which meant water was no longer being pumped out of the mine, which in turn put pressure on the company, Goldfields, who were running Wheal Jane. They also decided to pull out of the mine. The unions managed to persuade the government to pay to keep the Wheal Jane pumps active whilst new owners were sought to run the mine. By this stage mining photography was my main source of income and I joined the march to London. Although this was a serious time it was generally a happy crowd of miners and their supporters that I photographed.

In 1979 RTZ purchased both Mount Wellington and Wheal Jane and I was told that I could continue as the mine photographer. In 1984 Carnon the subsidiary company of RTZ purchased South Crofty allowing me to extend my mining experience. Of the many photographic assignments I had at Wheal Jane shaft sinking was the most challenging and interesting. However the County Adit had to be cleaned out and rebuilt in places which offered different challenges. I was also in the unique position to take a series of pictures explaining the raise boring process. The machine which you will see in this book is very similar to the one used to rescue the Chilean miners in autumn 2010.

People often ask me what you take photographs of in a mine. The photographs in this book are chosen as a cross section of the pictures I was commissioned to take over the lifespan of the mine.

If this book has aroused your curiosity about mining then more photographs and mining information can be found in my first book *Painting a Mine with Light*.

John Peck
2012

1
Photographs taken for the exhibition in 1972

A service tunnel being constructed in preparation for mining to begin.

Compressors on the surface supplying air which allows machinery to operate underground.

Opposite: A conveyor mixing the ore which has been brought to the surface. Following this process it will go the crusher and then on to the mill.

Ore being crushed ready for further processing.

The flotation floor in 1972.

Underground pumps on 9 level.

2
Raise Boring at Wheal Jane

A raise bore machine in operation in the mine. This is a rare underground photograph as it was taken using only available light. Note the drill strings in the foreground. These are one metre long rods which are connected together for the required drill length.

A miner drilling in a raise using conventional methods.

Opposite: The drill bit arriving at another level 60 metres below from where the raise bore machine is operating.

A photograph of a bearing from the raise borer. The picture was taken for insurance purposes as the wrong oil had been recommended by the oil company which resulted in damage to the bearing.

Opposite: This raise borer was one of only two machines which were operating in the UK. In the right of the picture is Jim Trew, underground Mine Manager, showing the machine to the press.

A miner fixing the footings on which the raise borer stands.

Opposite: The raise borer being serviced and tested before it goes underground.

The pilot bit about to commence drilling; note the water which is used for lubrication.

Opposite: The raise borer being operated.

The pilot bit having broken through is being examined for damage.

The breakthrough was expected at about 11.00pm. My wife was in Exeter for the week which meant I had to organise a baby sitter for the evening. However, when I had finished the job and was ready to go home I was informed the cage which would take me to the surface was broken and would not be ready until 2.00am. I was able to contact the baby sitter and let her know what was happening but she did not have a phone at home and could not contact her family. She did baby sit again after this incident!

The reamer being attached to the drill string; this will enable the rock to be cut to the right dimensions.

Left: The reamer, which is now fully dressed, has been lowered to show the first cut.

The reamer used in the rescue of the Chilean miners in 2010 was much smaller and was pushed down instead of being pulled up.

Opposite: A fitter is attaching a rod to a drill string of the raise borer

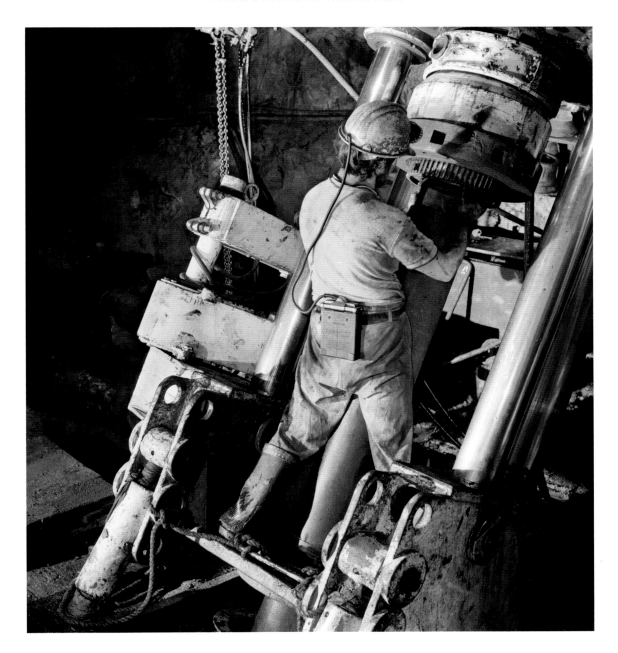

Above left: The reamer arrives back at the raise borer drilling its own footings!

Above right: The raise borer crew pose around the machine.

Opposite: This picture shows the fine tailing, the waste material produced by drawing the reamer upwards towards the raise borer. This is what the Chilean miners had to clear away during their miraculous escape in 2010.

I took this photograph to illustrate a shaft drilled by the raise borer. It had been broken into midway along its length providing a unique view. I was actually showing visitors around the mine and not on official photography duty.

Angry miners are attending a union meeting about the proposed closure by Goldfields of Wheal Jane.
Note the headgear in the background (above right).

In 1978 the mine was threatened with closure and the union organised a march to Parliament. Here the protesters are seen arriving at Paddington station.

The marchers gathering outside Paddington station preparing to commence their walk.

Miners walking through the streets of London. They are heading towards Hyde Park Corner, where the official demonstration will begin.

Miners rallying ready to commence their march on Parliament.

This page and opposite: The marchers heading down Park Lane; note that the miners and the police seem to be getting on very well.

The protesters on the train are returning to Cornwall predominantly optimistic about their futures. The beer cans (top) were stacked up after this miner fell asleep!

4
Mine refurbishment following a period of closure

The drive is being inspected in preparation for refurbishment of the mine c.1979. Note the Davy lamp (safety lamp) on the right hand side of the photograph. This was a necessary precaution needed until the mine was fully operational and good ventilation was ensured.

Opposite: This is a rare picture in a working mine. Over the closure period stalactites have formed.

Above: The mud you can see built up during this period and is covering the tracks the wagons use.

A new primary crusher is being installed.

Opposite: Here you can see the conveyor supports being refurbished. They had corroded when the mine was on the care and maintenance regime.

The tunnels have been cleaned and refurbished ready to be used again.

Opposite: The mill is in the process of being refurbished.

The concrete foundations ready for the new ball mill.

Opposite: The old ball mill is being taken away.

The new mill, still in the stage of being constructed.

Opposite: A conveyor is being constructed which will be used for moving the ore on the surface.

These photographs show the completed primary crushers ready for use.

5
Work taking place on the County Adit

A new loop in the county adit replacing a collapsed section.

This page and opposite: The ground is being prepared for the new portals of the County Adit. In the second photograph you can see the old mill at Mount Wellington. This now forms part of the mineral tramways from Portreath to Devoran.

Above left: Inside an old section of the county adit which is under the Wheal Maid valley.

Above right: Mine surveyors are measuring the angle of a lode to which the County Adit runs parallel.

6
Men working underground

A long hole stoping rig in operation.

Right: A long hole rig at work.

Opposite: Underhand stoping in B lode Wheal Jane

Two views of long hole stoping on 9 level. In order to take these photographs I had to stand in the open stope. I was standing in a pocket to protect me from the danger of possible falling rocks. The roof is 100 metres above my head.

Opposite: Waste material is being taken to the surface in a side tipping wagon.

A miner stands in the limelight.

Two miners posing for the camera.

A scoop tram working in the decline. These machines had powerful diesel engines but their catalytic converters were very efficient and only hot air came out of the exhaust.

A long haul dump truck, which collects the ore from the scoop trams.

Opposite: A surveyor posing in a shaft.

This page and opposite:
Photographs taken in a
sand filled stope. This was
an experiment to take the
waste from mining back
underground. The men are
busy constructing wooden
drains to remove the excess
water.

A photograph taken of machinery following an accident, the miner in the photograph is there purely for the purpose of scale.

Opposite: Miners preparing to work in the shaft. Note the netting which is bolted to the walls to prevent loose rocks falling.

A new tunnelling machine delivered and ready for use. The bright yellow colour gives away the fact that this machine has yet to be used.

A trackless mucker can be seen tipping ore into a raise.

Two photographs showing a remote-controlled trackless mucker being operated in a dangerous area

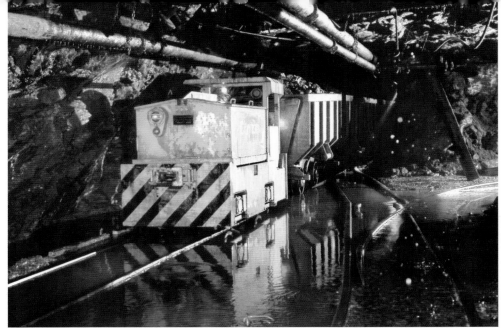

A Clayton locomotive hauling Granby wagons on 7 level.

Below: This is a relatively old wagon side-tipping into a grizzly.

A scoop tram working in the Wheal Maid decline.

Granby wagons being emptied into the grizzly.

7
Views underground

Ore being tipped into a raise by a trackless compressed-air-operated tipper on its way to the crusher.

This page and opposite: A scraper operating in a stope. It is pushing the ore which has been produced by blasting into a raise. This machine could only operate in stopes at a maximum angle of 45 degrees.

Stoping in the higher levels of Wheal Jane where the stopes were approximately at angles of 45 degrees.

Above left: A schoolroom deep underground used to introduce miners to safe mining practices.

Above right: Drilling prior to blasting in a stope.

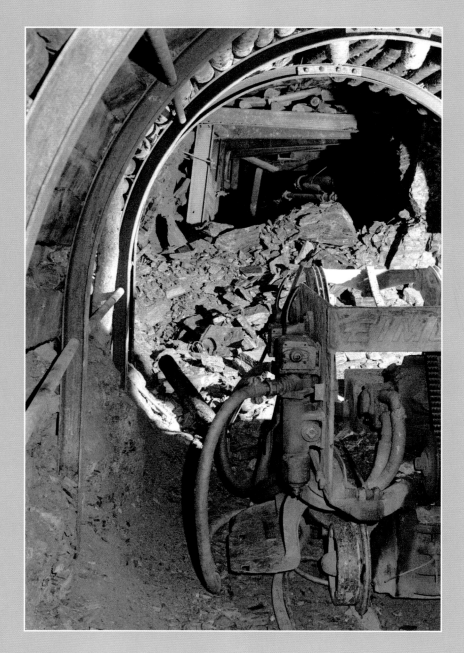

A photograph taken after an accident. In this case the roof supports were being fitted to make the area safer when the roof collapsed.

Opposite: Wooden sets which have been erected to secure loose ground.

These pictures were taken when the mine was on a care and maintenance regime following the proposed closure.

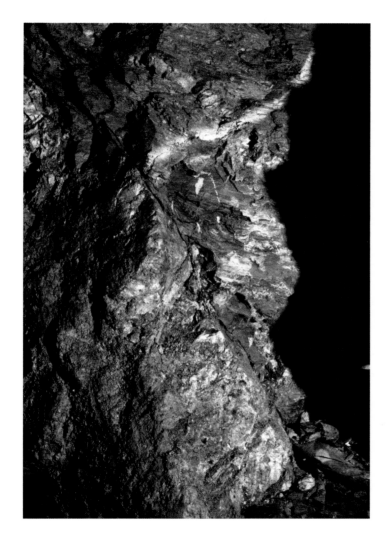

Pump station.

Whilst passing thorough the old workings in Mount Wellington Mine. I saw some Cousin Jacks, which I stopped to photograph. These are the old method of loading wagons from the stope.

The pump station Wheal Jane.

Ventilation fans, on 6 level Mount Wellington, which are 1.5 metres in diameter.

A water tight door protecting 15 level. It was always an unnerving experience passing through and I dreaded the thought of them closing behind me.

A new decline the purpose of which was to bring ore from below 15 level to the crusher.

8
Surface photographs

The following images are a series of aerial photographs taken in February 1984. The first picture (above) shows the head gear and the second picture (overleaf) shows the mill in the foreground.

The portals to the Wheal Maid decline.

A view of Mount Wellington. The village of Twlelveheads can be seen on the right.

Opposite: Inside the mill, showing the floatation cells with the control panels behind them.

Zinc concentrate being loaded on to a boat at Newham Quay, Truro.

The lorry is being loaded with zinc concentrate outside the mill at Wheal Jane.

Opposite: The floatation floor in the mill.

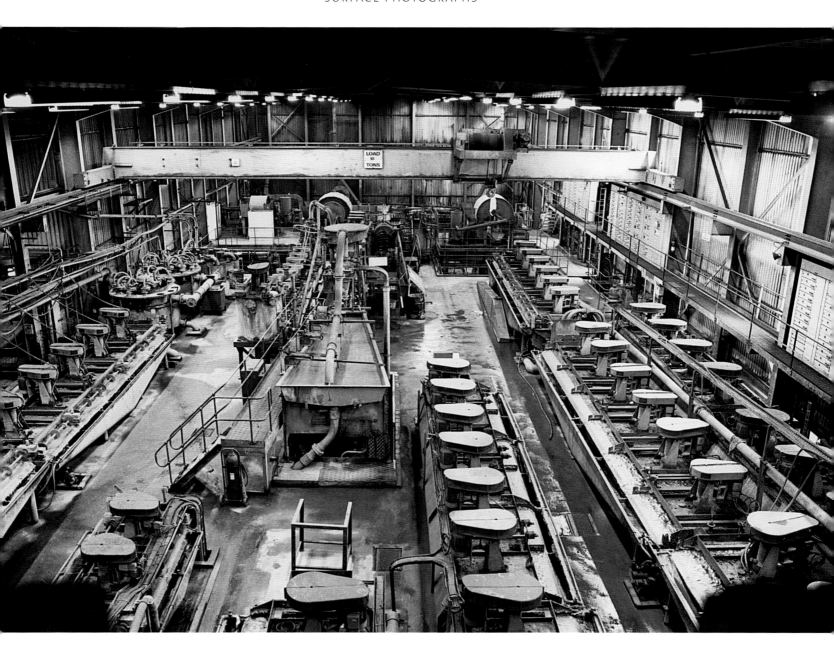

A view of the mill looking across the dam; note the many seagulls taking refuge from rough weather at sea.

A shaking table in the mill.

Here you can see the tailings dam with the mill in the back ground.

Tailings dam looking south-west from the mill.

The tug of war team on their return from competing in South Africa

Wheal Jane snooker team May 1984.

The Wheal Jane Special team photographed prior to their match against Portugal which took place at Truro rugby club.
March 1984.

These photographs (pages 102-105) show work being undertaken to stabilise the dam.

The official opening of the mine. This photograph was quickly taken on the 1 October 1971 as I was out walking. I was unaware of what was happening but could see some sort of celebration taking place and thought it would be a good photograph. A year later I became the mine photographer!

New headgear being erected.

In this photograph the last section of the new headgear is being put into place.

A wagon in the cage is ready to be lowered for loading.

A meeting in the boardroom at the offices in Wheal Jane.

A view which shows Clemmow Shaft next to the compressor station, with the primary crusher attached to the conveyors. The mill can be seen in the background.

A panoramicview of the Wheal Jane site looking east, with Baldhu church on the left and the Carnon Valley viaduct on the right (Truro–Falmouth line).

Mount Wellington mine in the foreground and Wheal Jane in the distance, with Nangiles in between. The main lode ran through all three mines in the direction of this photograph.

A Clayton locomotive on the surface in the battery shed.

A panoramic view taken in the valley below Wellington Mine, the men in the distance are holding a meeting to discuss a drainage problem. There is a danger that the Carnon River will flow into the mine. In the foreground the track you can see now forms part of the Devoran to Portreath mineral tramway.

One of my regular jobs was to photograph views of the Wheal Maid and Carnon valleys. This is a view taken from Hale Mills looking towards Twelveheads and Bissoe. This was taken in April 1984.

New Granby wagons ready for work underground.

Nº.2 SHAFT SIGNAL CODE

SIGNAL	ACTION
1	STOP WHEN IN MOTION
1	RAISE-WHEN STATIONARY
2	LOWER
3	MEN ABOUT TO TRAVEL
6 PAUSE 1	SLOWLY RAISE
6 PAUSE 2	SLOWLY LOWER
7	PLEASE REPEAT SIGNAL
8	CONTINUOUS ROCK HOISTING COMMENCING
9	MATERIALS TO BE LOADED
6 PAUSE 7	TIPPING STATION-PLATFORM
6 PAUSE 8	BANK-COLLAR
4 PAUSE 1	MEZZANINE
4 PAUSE 2	2 LEVEL
4 PAUSE 3	3 LEVEL
4 PAUSE 4	4 LEVEL
4 PAUSE 5	5 LEVEL
4 PAUSE 6	6 LEVEL
4 PAUSE 7	7 LEVEL
4 PAUSE 8	8 LEVEL
4 PAUSE 9	9 LEVEL
4 PAUSE 10	10 LEVEL
5 PAUSE 1	11 LEVEL
5 PAUSE 2	12 LEVEL
4 PAUSE 11	ADIT LEVEL
10	CAGE CLEAR
12	SHAFT INSPECTION ABOUT TO START (MECHANICAL SIGNAL)
13	ACCIDENT
14	ELECTRICIAN TESTING

MAXIMUM CAGE CAPACITY 40 MEN

The shaft signal code board.

9
Shaft sinking

A winch being installed in preparation for shaft sinking on 10 level.

A travelling cage constructed to allow work in the shaft.

This photograph shows a workstation on 10 level which is the division between the current working level of the mine and from where the shaft sinking will take place.

Taken on 11 level preparing to commence shaft sinking.

Right: This mechanism controls the swinging of the kibble in the shaft.

The men are clearing the mud which has built up in the sump to enable shaft sinking to commence.

The kibble is the only means of transport down the shaft while the sinking proceeds. Officially it carried three men in the bucket; however it wasn't unknown for three others to be standing on the rim. I had to use this means of transport with all my photographic equipment to reach the site. The pipe above the kibble is blowing fresh air into the shaft.

A submersible pump is being lowered into the water which will pump water to the surface. All my equipment had to be waterproofed to allow me to work in this environment.

Once the miners are down the shaft the same kibble is used to haul the rock back up.

Once the cactus grab has picked up the rocks it has to be physically swung by the men to be emptied into the kibble.

A station being built; the new shaft can be seen in the background.

Opposite: The walls of the shaft being created; we are now below 13 level.

Cement is being poured into the shuttering in order to create the walls of the shaft.

Opposite: Water seeping through rocks was a general hazard in this mine. Here the men are pumping liquid cement into the walls prior to shuttering.

Steel girders are being set in place to provide a floor for the new crusher.

Opposite: Tools and compressed air arriving to allow the sinking process to continue.

The crusher is being lowered onto the girders.

The crusher station is being completed.

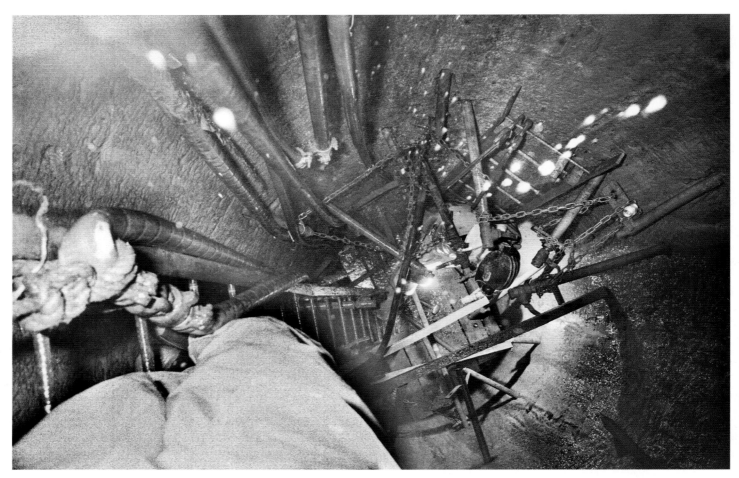

This is an ore pass to the crusher which is being long-hole grouted to prevent water ingress.

Politicians visit the mine and we march to London again

These photographs were taken whilst on a march in London to hand in a petition at 10 Downing Street. This was an attempt to stave off closure as the price of tin had been falling, putting a question mark on the future of Cornish tin mining. A series of photographs were taken of various politicians who visited the mine whilst it was under the threat.

A group of Truro Councillors.

David Owen MP.

Roy Hattersley MP.

David Harris MP.